SINBAD
SAILING INTO PERIL

AN
ARABIAN
TALE

STORY BY
MARIE P CROALL

PENCILS AND INKS BY
CLINT HILINSKI

OTTOMAN
EMPIRE
(TURKEY)

MEDITERRANEAN

SEA

THE
MIDDLE EAST

THIS MAP SHOWS THE MIDDLE EAST AS IT WAS
KNOWN AROUND AD 1500, WHEN THE SINBAD
STORIES WERE COLLECTED AND WRITTEN IN ARABIC.

SINBAD

SAILING INTO PERIL

AN ARABIAN TALE

BAGHDAD

PERSIA
(IRAN)

MESOPOTAMIA
(IRAQ)

River Tigris

River Euphrates

BASSORAH
(BASRA)

ARABIA
(SAUDI ARABIA)

LERNER BOOKS · LONDON · NEW YORK · MINNEAPOLIS

Sinbad is a character in Arabian Nights, a classic work of Arabian literature. Also known as The Thousand and One Nights, the book is made up of approximately 200 tales from Persia, India and other nations in and near the Middle East. The Arabian Nights stories were collected and written down in Arabic around ad 1500. In the 1880s, British scholars Sir Richard F Burton and John Payne translated the stories into English. Featuring enchanting characters and amazing story lines, the tales have captured readers' imaginations for generations.

In adapting the story of Sinbad, author Marie P Croall worked from Arabian Nights Volume I: The Marvels and Wonders of the Thousand and One Nights, adapted from Richard F Burton's unexpurgated translation by Jack Zipes. Artist Clint Hilinski consulted numerous historical resources and collaborated with Allan T Kohl, an art historian and visual resources librarian at the Minneapolis College of Art and Design, USA. Kohl has studied the Arabian Nights tales and authored an article on Sinbad for Medieval Trade, Travel and Exploration: An Encyclopedia.

STORY BY MARIE P CROALL

PENCILS AND INKS BY CLINT HILINSKI

COLOURING BY HI-FI DESIGN

LETTERING BY BILL HAUSER

CONSULTANT: ALLAN T KOHL, MA, MINNEAPOLIS COLLEGE OF ART AND DESIGN

Graphic Universe™ is a trademark of Lerner Publishing Group, Inc.

First published in the United Kingdom in 2009 by
Lerner Books,
Dalton House,
60 Windsor Avenue,
London SW19 2RR

Website address: www.lernerbooks.co.uk

This edition was updated and edited for UK publication by Discovery Books Ltd., First Floor 2 College Street, Ludlow, Shropshire SY8 1AN

British Library Cataloguing in Publication Data

Croall, Marie P
  Sinbad : sailing into peril. - 2nd ed. - (Graphic universe)
  1. Sindbad the Sailor (Legendary character) - Comic books,
  strips, etc. - Juvenile fiction 2. Children's stories - Comic books, strips, etc.
  I. Title II. Hilinski, Clint
  741.5

ISBN-13: 978 0 7613 4350 9

Printed in Singapore

TABLE OF CONTENTS

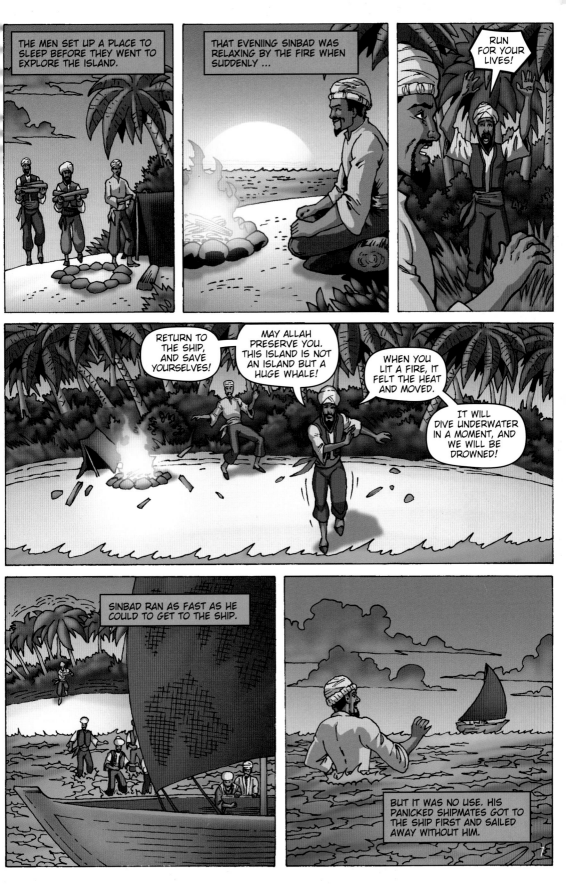

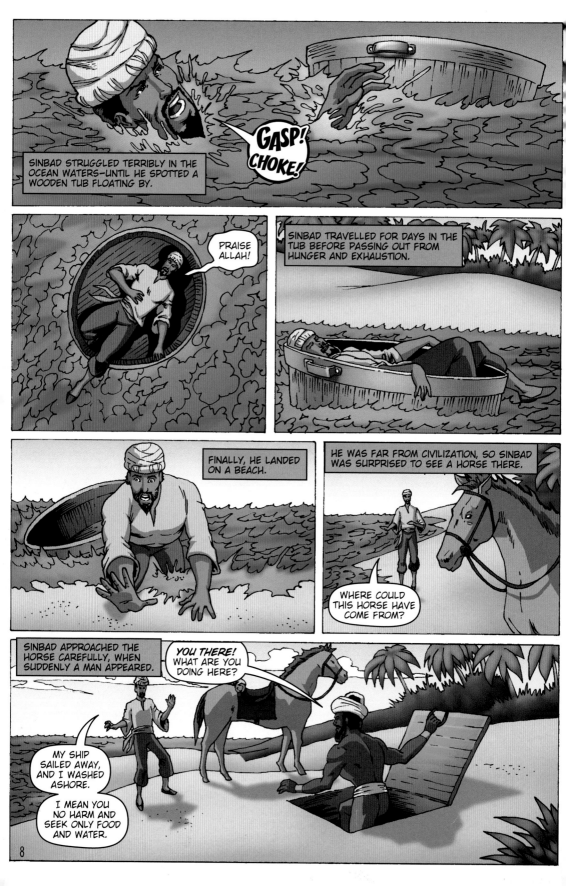

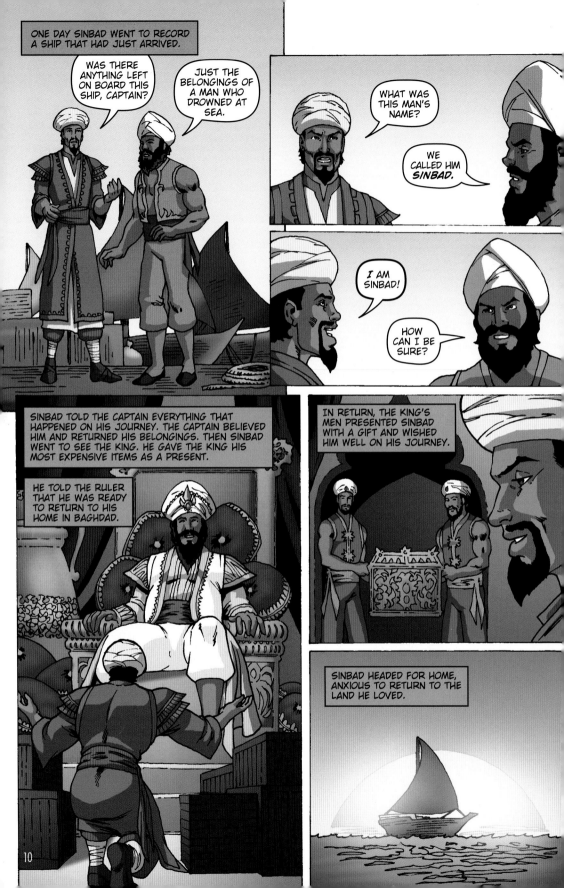

SINBAD AND THE RUKH

ARE YOU READY FOR ANOTHER TALE, HUSBAND?

CERTAINLY, MY DEAR WIFE. TELL ME WHAT HAPPENS TO SINBAD NEXT.

BEFORE TOO LONG, SINBAD GREW TIRED OF LIFE AT HOME AND STRUCK OUT ON ANOTHER JOURNEY.

THE SHIP ANCHORED SO THE MEN COULD EXPLORE A NEWLY DISCOVERED ISLAND.

AFTER WALKING AROUND THE ISLAND FOR A WHILE, SINBAD GREW SLEEPY AND STOPPED TO TAKE A QUICK NAP.

BUT WHEN HE AWOKE, HE FOUND THAT THE SHIP HAD LEFT WITHOUT HIM.

HE WAS DESERTED ON THE STRANGE ISLAND.

SINBAD EXPLORED THE REST OF THE ISLAND AND FOUND SOMETHING STRANGE.

AFTER EXAMINING THE OBJECT CAREFULLY, HE RECOGNIZED IT AS A RUKH'S EGG, HAVING HEARD STORIES ABOUT THE HUGE BIRDS.

PRAISE ALLAH ...

LOOKING AT THE RUKH, SINBAD CAME UP WITH A WAY TO GET OFF THE ISLAND.

AFTER USING HIS TURBAN TO TIE HIMSELF TO THE BIRD, SINBAD WAS CARRIED AWAY.

THE RUKH DROPPED SINBAD ON A ROCKY CLIFF.

SINBAD NOTICED DIAMONDS ON THE GROUND. HE WAS SURPRISED TO FIND GEMS IN THIS LOCATION.

SINBAD AND THE OGRE

BUT SINBAD WAS READY FOR MORE ADVENTURE. HE SOON PLANNED ANOTHER TRIP.

WE'VE SAILED OFF COURSE AND ARE TOO NEAR THE MOUNTAIN OF THE ZUGHB.

NO MAN HAS EVER COME AWAY FROM THERE ALIVE.

NO SOONER HAD THE CAPTAIN SPOKEN THAN *APES* LEAPED ONTO THE BOAT.

ALLAH, SAVE US!

THE APES TOOK CONTROL OF THE SHIP AND LEFT SINBAD AND HIS MEN ON THE MOUNTAIN.

THE MEN HAD TO EXPLORE THE ISLAND. THEY WERE HUNGRY AND HAD TO FIND FOOD.

JUST BEFORE DARK, THEY FOUND A LARGE CASTLE.

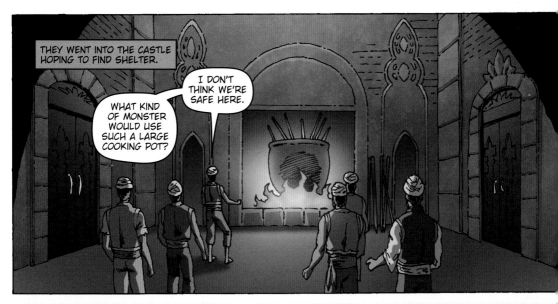

THEY WENT INTO THE CASTLE HOPING TO FIND SHELTER.

WHAT KIND OF MONSTER WOULD USE SUCH A LARGE COOKING POT?

I DON'T THINK WE'RE SAFE HERE.

THE EXHAUSTED MEN HAD NO CHOICE BUT TO SLEEP IN THE CASTLE. SINBAD AND ANOTHER MAN KEPT WATCH.

BEFORE LONG, AN EVIL CREATURE APPEARED.

AN OGRE! ALLAH, SAVE US!

THE MEN WATCHED IN HORROR AS THE OGRE TOOK THE CAPTAIN.

THE MEN KNEW THEY HAD TO FIND A WAY OFF THE ISLAND.

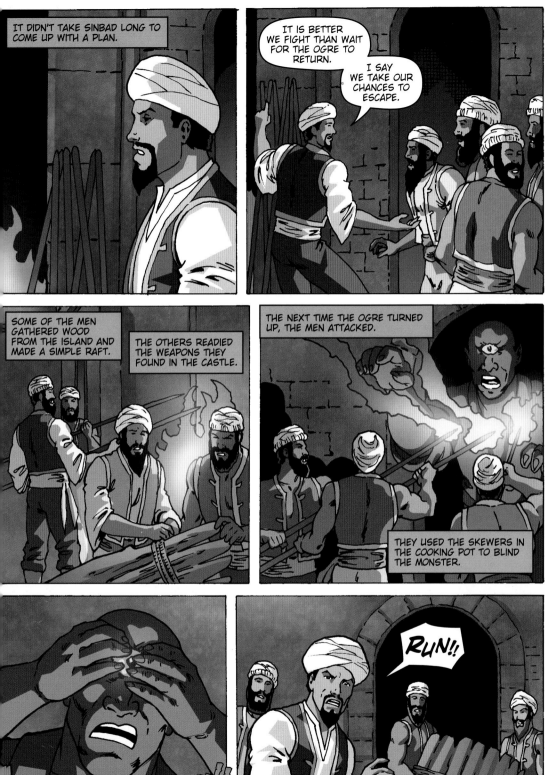

IT DIDN'T TAKE SINBAD LONG TO COME UP WITH A PLAN.

IT IS BETTER WE FIGHT THAN WAIT FOR THE OGRE TO RETURN.

I SAY WE TAKE OUR CHANCES TO ESCAPE.

SOME OF THE MEN GATHERED WOOD FROM THE ISLAND AND MADE A SIMPLE RAFT.

THE OTHERS READIED THE WEAPONS THEY FOUND IN THE CASTLE.

THE NEXT TIME THE OGRE TURNED UP, THE MEN ATTACKED.

THEY USED THE SKEWERS IN THE COOKING POT TO BLIND THE MONSTER.

RRRRRRGGGH!!

RUN!!

17

SINBAD WAS SAFE FROM THE SNAKE THAT NIGHT, BUT HE KNEW HE HAD TO GET OFF THE ISLAND.

HE TRIED TO ESCAPE.

BUT THERE WAS NOWHERE TO GO. SOON HE WAS NEAR DEATH FROM HUNGER.

JUST WHEN HE THOUGHT HE WAS FINISHED ...

PRAISE ALLAH! A SHIP! I AM RESCUED!

HELP! OVER HERE!

THE MERCHANTS ON THE SHIP WERE ONLY TOO HAPPY TO RESCUE HIM AND BRING HIM BACK TO BAGHDAD.

AT HOME SINBAD TOLD HIS STORY TO HIS AWESTRUCK FRIENDS.

BUT HE KNEW HE HAD NOT YET TAKEN HIS LAST JOURNEY.

SINBAD WALKED ON THROUGH THE NIGHT, WAITING FOR A WAY TO GET RID OF THE MAN.

HE SAW SOME BERRIES NEARBY AND CAME UP WITH AN IDEA.

SINBAD SQUEEZED JUICE FROM THE BERRIES INTO A HOLLOW GOURD.

THEN HE WAITED FOR THE JUICE TO FERMENT.

WHEN THE TIME WAS RIGHT, HE PULLED OUT THE GOURD.

I COULD DO WITH A *NIIIICE ... COOOOL ...* DRINK!

SINBAD HAD ESCAPED FROM THE MAN, BUT HE STILL HAD NO WAY TO GET OFF THE ISLAND.

HE MADE A SHELTER AND ATE WHAT FRUIT HE COULD FIND. HE PREPARED TO SPEND A LONG TIME ON THE ISLAND.

SINBAD STAYED ON THE ISLAND FOR MORE DAYS THAN HE COULD COUNT.

HE BECAME CONTENT WITH HIS SIMPLE LIFE.

THEN ONE DAY, SINBAD SAW A WONDERFUL SIGHT.

A SHIP!

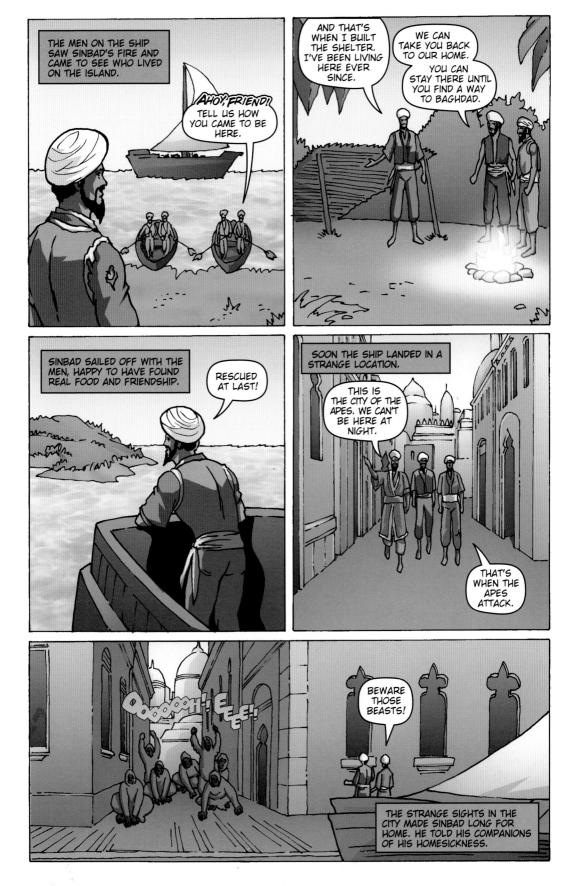

THE WHALE MOVED IN FRONT OF THE SHIP, READY TO SWALLOW IT WHOLE.

AS THE MEN PRAYED FOR HELP, A FIERCE STORM PULLED THE SHIP FROM THE WHALE.

THE STORM TOSSED THE SHIP INTO A ROCKY REEF.

TERRIFIED, SINBAD MADE A PROMISE.

IF ALLAH SAVES ME, I WILL NEVER AGAIN TRAVEL ON THE HIGH SEAS!

I WILL NEVER AGAIN SUFFER FOR MY GREED.

I WILL BUILD ANOTHER RAFT, AND IF I AM SAVED, IT WILL BE BY ALLAH'S GRACE.

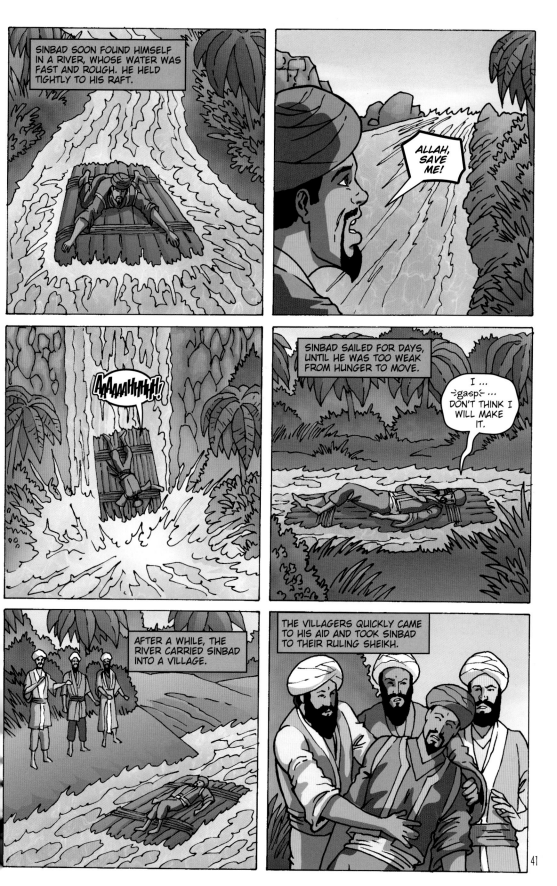

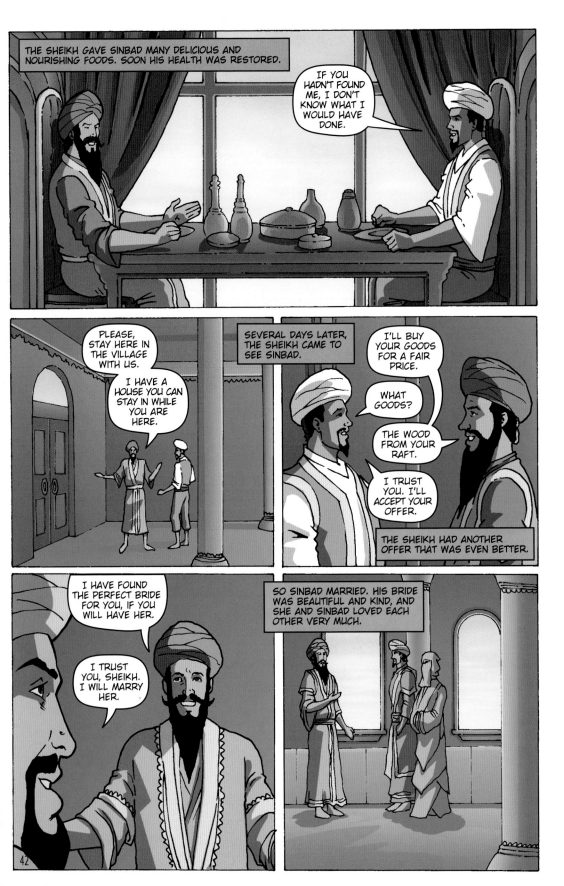

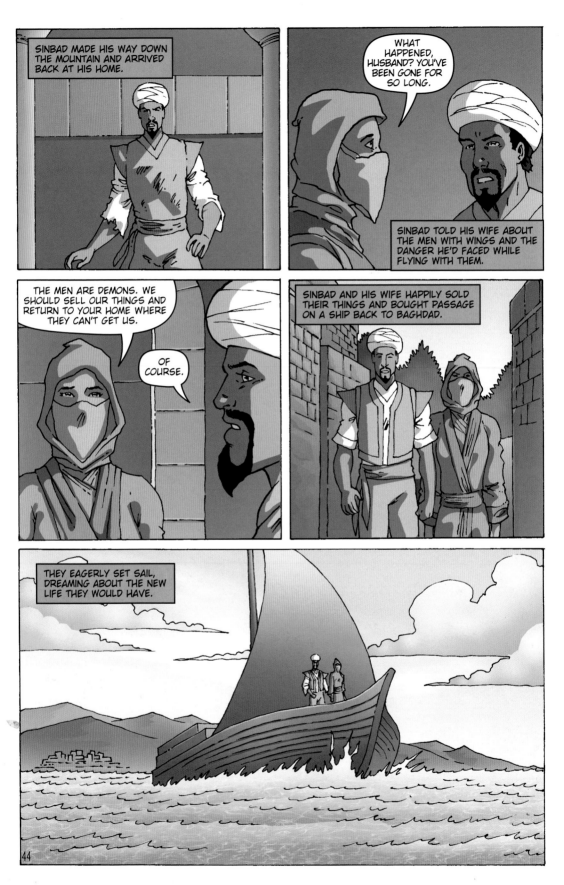

SINBAD MADE HIS WAY DOWN THE MOUNTAIN AND ARRIVED BACK AT HIS HOME.

WHAT HAPPENED, HUSBAND? YOU'VE BEEN GONE FOR SO LONG.

SINBAD TOLD HIS WIFE ABOUT THE MEN WITH WINGS AND THE DANGER HE'D FACED WHILE FLYING WITH THEM.

THE MEN ARE DEMONS. WE SHOULD SELL OUR THINGS AND RETURN TO YOUR HOME WHERE THEY CAN'T GET US.

OF COURSE.

SINBAD AND HIS WIFE HAPPILY SOLD THEIR THINGS AND BOUGHT PASSAGE ON A SHIP BACK TO BAGHDAD.

THEY EAGERLY SET SAIL, DREAMING ABOUT THE NEW LIFE THEY WOULD HAVE.

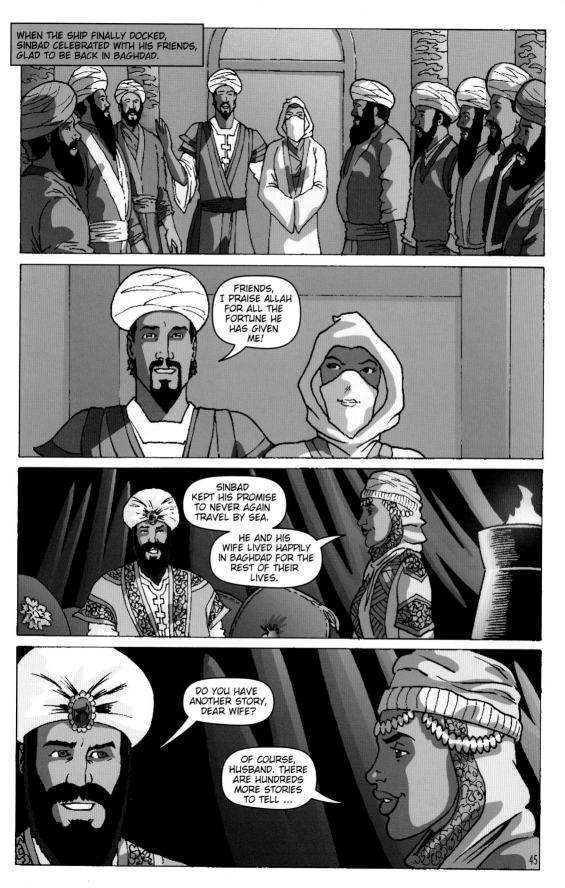

GLOSSARY

ALLAH: the name for God in the Islamic faith

BAGHDAD: a city in the Middle Eastern country of Iraq. Baghdad is the country's capital.

BASSORAH: a city and port in the Middle Eastern country of Iraq. In modern times, Bassorah is called Basra.

CALIPH: a ruler in an Islamic community

FERMENT: to go through a chemical change. Fermentation is used to make different kinds of food and drinks.

GEM: a valuable stone

GOURD: a fruit with a round shape. Gourds are similar to pumpkins and squash.

MERCHANT: someone who makes money by selling goods

OGRE: a fierce monster

PORT: a place where boats and ships dock

REEF: a strip of coral, rock or sand near the surface of a body of water

RUKH: a mythical bird of great size and strength. Rukhs are said to live near the Indian Ocean.

SCHEHERAZADE: the narrator of the *Arabian Nights* tales. She tells stories to her husband, the sultan, to win his favour and prove her worth.

SHEIKH: the leader of an Arab tribe or village

SULTAN: a king in some Muslim countries

TURBAN: a head covering made by winding a scarf around the head

FURTHER READING AND WEBSITES

Downing, David. *The Making of the Middle East* Raintree, 2006. Learn about the Middle East – the region of the world where the *Arabian Nights* began.

Fletcher, Susan. *Shadow Spinner* Bloomsbury Publishing, 1999. In this novel, a girl named Marjan saves Scheherazade from the sultan when the storyteller runs out of tales.

Global Connections: The Middle East
http://www.pbs.org/wgbh/globalconnections/mideast/index.html
On this website, you'll find a timeline of Middle Eastern history as well as interesting information on the region's people and culture.

Leeson, Robert. *My Sister Shahrazad: Tales from the Arabian Nights* Frances Lincoln, 2003. This volume includes stories such as *The Fisherman and the Jinni* and *The Dream*.

Walser, David. *The Thousand Nights and One Night* Puffin Books, 2007. Welcome to an ancient world of enchantment and adventure where animals talk and genies grant wishes. David Walser retells these fantastic tales alongside beautiful illustrations by Jan Pienkowski.

CREATING *SINBAD: SAILING INTO PERIL*

In creating this story, author Marie P Croall worked from *Arabian Nights Volume I: The Marvels and Wonders of the Thousand and One Nights*, adapted from Richard F Burton's unexpurgated translation by Jack Zipes. Artist Clint Hilinski worked in consultation with art historian Allan T Kohl and used historical sources to shape the visual content of the tale. Together the text and artwork tell the story of Sinbad, a man who encountered many adventures and hardships in his travels on the high seas.

original pencil sketch from page 18

INDEX

ABOUT THE AUTHOR AND THE ARTIST

MARIE P CROALL lives in Cary, North Carolina, USA with her loving husband and four wonderful cats. She has written for Marvel, DC Comics, Moonstone Books, Devils Due and Harris Comics. She has also completed a self-published graphic novel and a short film. Croall has spent much of her life reading fables and legends from the Middle East and Asia and enjoys discovering new things about different cultures.

CLINT HILINSKI grew up in Esko, Minnesota, USA where he became interested in art at an early age. He continued studying art at the University of Wisconsin-Superior, where he received his bachelor's degree in fine art. Hilinski's influences include Jim Lee, Alan Davis and Adam Hughes. He has worked as an illustrator for DC Comics, Image, Dark Horse and many other companies. Hilinski has worked on titles such as *Justice League of America*, *Xena*, *Voltron* and *GI Joe*.

First published in the United States of America in 2008
Copyright © 2008 by Lerner Publishing Group, Inc.